Double trou..... living with manic depression

a personal story and practical guide

by Pauline Rhodes

Fourems Publications

Published by Fourems Publications, Hertford, UK

First Published 2007

ISBN 978-0-9529765-6-1

Grateful thanks to the following:
Book sponsors:

sanofi aventis

Because health matters

Cover design: Mixed Images, Hitchin, Herts.
Design visuals: Heather Jukes
Proof reading: Alan Nicholls
for their generous support.

Printed by Piggott Black Bear Limited, Cambridge, UK

The contents of this book are based solely on personal experience.
The author has no medical qualifications and anyone requiring
advice about manic depression or issues surrounding it should seek
help from a registered medical practitioner. This book is intended to
help the families of, and those caring for, sufferers understand more
about living with this very complex illness.
The information given in this book is believed to be correct, but the
author, the publisher and their agents cannot accept responsibility
for any errors or omissions or any direct or indirect consequences
thereof, however caused.

In memory of Eric Scott 1920 - 2007

Dedication
This book is dedicated to all those less fortunate than me, whose homes and families have been destroyed by mental illness, who have been deserted by friends and feel isolated and alone with their illness and those with family members suffering from it.
In order to help others, a donation from the sale of each copy will be made to a mental health charity.

Acknowledgements
I would like to thank everyone involved in helping me to come to terms with my illness and to produce this book, especially Julie Dennison who inspired me to try again, and Eric Scott, my great friend, editor and publisher, who made sure I succeeded at my second attempt.
Above all, I would like to thank Nigel, Jenny and Helen, who have lived through the story so far. They have been wonderfully supportive and without them, all my family and close friends, and my outstanding GP, Dr. Jan Cembala, I am certain I would not have lived to write it.

Contents

Some background to Manic Depression/Bipolar Affective Disorder 1

Respectable, efficient, successful career woman 5

Motherhood and the birth of "double trouble" 10

Rock bottom – life in a psychiatric unit 16

Struggling to stay afloat – "you don't look like a psychiatric patient!" 22

The death of my father – another spell in hell 26

Paralysed by fear and frustration, prone to panic attacks 31

Music and lyrics – comfort and escapism 35

Doctors, consultants and alternative therapists 39

Pushing back the boundaries: assessing my achievements 43

The role of religion – A test of faith? 48

Starting work again and more volunteering 52

Moving forward – creating new challenges 55

The death of my mother - two more weeks of hell 58

Loving, hating and lashing out 62

Picking up the pieces and facing the future - learning to ignore labels – working for Rethink 66

Keep fit, keep taking the tablets and hope for the best 70

A blessing in disguise – compassionate teenagers! 74

1. Some background to Manic Depression/Bipolar Affective Disorder

What do Stephen Fry, Winston Churchill, Spike Milligan, Frank Bruno and this author have in common? We have all suffered from Manic Depression.

I was surprised to discover so many famous people were sufferers, but I was equally surprised that around one in a hundred people in Britain are diagnosed as having manic depression (now often called Bipolar Affective Disorder) – and with a population of almost 60 million that means there are about 600,000 people suffering from it, so it is more common than many people think.

It is a serious mental health problem but, like a number of others, it is one which affects sufferers in ways which mean they often deny they are ill. It causes extreme mood swings and affects people very differently. Some experience more manic episodes where they feel incredibly well, vibrant, generous, and full of energy which, in my experience, has resulted in being sectioned under the Mental Health Act and consigned to a psychiatric unit under sedation! Others will experience more depressive phases where they are at the bottom of a black pit with no escape. The isolation of this is terrifying and the sense of hopelessness and despair indescribable and unbearable and I have known several people who have committed suicide during one of these phases.

Manic Depression is not a disease which can be caught. It can strike anyone at any time. It is often triggered by bereavement or other major life stresses, such as redundancy or divorce, but it can be a culmination of mental health problems such as severe depression or overpowering anxiety. There is a theory that some people are born with a tendency towards it, but this does **not** mean it will necessarily run in families.

Mine began life as an illness called "manic puerperal psychosis" which literally means a manic illness developed within six weeks of giving birth. Having given birth to twins by emergency Caesarean, had some ovarian cysts removed, had my sacra ileac joint displaced, suffered a massive haematoma which dispersed through the skin of my stomach and suffered paralysis through post operative shock – I was not feeling at my best but little did I know that as soon as I started to feel full of energy and find myself awake most of the night making plans for our future, I was embarking on this strange illness. I was told when I was diagnosed that I was one in a million – because manic puerperal psychosis was such a rare illness. The Royal College of Psychiatrists now say " puerperal psychosis is rather rare and happens after only 1 in 500 births". So having spent two weeks in a maternity unit I was discharged only to be expected to be separated from my babies and sent to a psychiatric unit (which had a mother and baby unit that could only take one baby!) Naturally I refused and I was treated at home by my family doctor with much help and support from my family and friends. However when my twins were 13 months old I spent almost three months sectioned alone in the unit, which was hell. It has since been diagnosed as manic depression and more lately bipolar affective disorder but to me the name is immaterial. It seems most forms of mental illness have many facets in common. The important part has been learning to cope with the illness.

A doctor once explained to me that my mind was "playing tricks on me" and whilst during a manic attack this seems unbelievable, it seems equally unlikely when you are in the depths of despair! Having said that, it is true your own mind is deluding you. The other problem is that this, in itself, undermines your confidence, you don't know what to believe and can find yourself constantly searching for "normality".

I have likened my illness, which began 16 years ago, to being stuck in a lift with no control over where the doors will open. Even now I live in fear that the lift will start moving and stop either on the top floor or in the basement and I will find myself being sectioned once more.

Many people suffer far more extreme episodes than I. Some live in a semi-permanent state of hyper-activity and mania while others spend years in depression. I am lucky because my illness responds to medication and is generally controlled by daily doses of Lithium Carbonate but despite this I have been sectioned four times and spent months in psychiatric units. Because of this my bouts of illness have been interspersed with long periods of "normality" and I believe this is also quite common.

In order to help control my mood swings I have become tee-total because alcohol induces both mania and depression and I dare not risk destabilising my fragile mental state. This was quite hard when I began, but it does make me popular as a "taxi driver" and it is quite enjoyable watching other people getting drunk and suffering from hangovers!

There are many different treatments available many of which are long term. Because of my use of Lithium Carbonate, I have regular blood tests and I have to be very careful of other drugs having an interaction. Over the years I have tried counselling, complementary therapies and herbal remedies as well as exercise, anti-psychotic drugs and sleeping tablets. I have found listening to music, silk painting and writing therapeutic but even now when I am awake at 2 or 3 o'clock in the morning I can have flashbacks to the nightmares I have experienced.

Having said all that, in some ways the illness has enriched my life. It has given me a fascinating insight into the power of the human mind. It has enabled me to empathise with others suffering from severe mental illness and to offer them some comfort and hope and it has given my life a new dimension. Never again will I take good health for granted.

A word of caution about "Lithium":
If you are prescribed either **Lithium Carbonate** or **Lithium Citrate** to treat manic depression, make sure you do not mix the two. Due to unforeseen circumstances, I did, and suffered some unpleasant side effects!

2. Respectable, efficient, successful career woman

Me, in 1980 before the illness. Photography courtesy of Kingsley Michael

Up until I gave birth I was pursuing a career in editing and public relations and my CV cited my key skills as an efficient administrator/organiser/co-ordinator; effective communicator at all levels; logical and creative thinking, while the personal qualities it listed were being well organised; self motivated; conscientious and having a sense of humour. I mention this because although it was, and is, true to a certain extent, I have been told that when I am in a manic phase I am almost like a caricature of my self – my strengths and weaknesses are all amplified. When I am manic it is almost like looking at a sequin through a kaleidoscope. Everything looks very different, it is vivid, colourful and vibrant and you can see dimensions to it you have never seen before.

Certainly, when I am in a manic phase, I am aware of a desperate need to get my life back in order whether that be through tidying, filing or making lists. I know that I try to use my excess energy to restore order around me. To others it simply appears I am causing chaos. I certainly cannot perceive the reality that the chaos is in my brain and no amount of tidying will get rid of it! Like most women, I also enjoy shopping and when I am manic I tend to go on spending sprees buying presents for people because I know my illness is upsetting them. I know irrational shopping sprees are often a tangible facet of mania.

It has been suggested that living and working as I did, for over 10 years, to strict deadlines has meant that my life already had manic and depressive tendencies in it. I certainly know I lived on plenty of adrenalin to meet all the deadlines and found myself on something of "a high" when I met them and then tended to dip into negativity until I faced the next challenge but I really don't believe that this contributed to the onset of the illness. I had never intended to return to work full time after the birth of my twins, but I always thought I would keep my professional life ticking over with some freelance work.

Having said that, realising that it would not be sensible to resume my previous career was a great blow and I did feel a very real sense of loss. I did do some freelance work when the twins were about two, in an effort to drag myself out of depression, but I found the combination of deadlines, toddlers and illness didn't work – even when we employed help with childcare. Interestingly, just three years ago, in 2003, I was commissioned to write a series of articles for a local magazine which were published, but I found the world I returned to very different from the one I left in October 1989. Technology had moved on and I had to submit my articles on CD-ROM. I was also required to supply my own photographs, which needed to be taken on a digital camera – all of which I managed, but was a far cry from the typewriter and carbon paper I had to use when I was training!

I remember reading my CV many years ago and wondering what happened to the person I was. I also found it very strange to realise that very few people that I know now actually knew what I was like then. Certainly my daughters have never known me working full-time to deadlines and going to press conferences and public relations launches, but when I look back now I feel that those days were enjoyable but false. In that world most people were "plastic", everyone said "Hi, how are you?" and everyone replied "Hi, I'm fine!" No one really knew the people beneath the professional façade and I find meeting and getting to know real people much more rewarding.

I have also found that over the years many of the qualities I listed on my CV are still there but I am using them in a different way. The one which I completely lose during my illness is my sense of humour and I often feel this is the one I would benefit from most whether I am manic or depressed! In fact, I have a lifelong friend who says I'm never mentally ill I just suffer from a massive sense of humour failure. She has suggested "a raunchy novel and a stay in a health farm" would be the best medicine for me and I often think she has a good point!

The onset of manic depression certainly gave me many feelings of guilt and worthlessness and when you are deprived of your freedom (through being sectioned) and find yourself dumped in a psychiatric unit with just the clothes you are wearing, it is hard not to feel a helpless victim with no self esteem and no self confidence. Having to borrow money from a complete stranger to make a phone call home to request some clean underwear is degrading and demoralising and is certainly something that I never expected to have to do. I am sure there must be a better way of treating people with mental illness.

From my voluntary work at my local hospice I see the dignity accorded to people with cancer and I often feel that none of us chooses to have one illness rather than another, so why should people suffering from mental illness be subjected to such stigma, fear and degradation while those with cancer receive the very best? (Having said that, I don't, for one moment, feel that the cancer patients don't deserve their treatment, only that the disparity seems so unfair on others).

I have often felt that my illness might just as well be called "schizophrenia" because when I am very ill, I feel that I am a far cry from the respectable, efficient, successful career woman I once was, and I find it hard to relate to that person when I am locked up with an eclectic mix of people suffering from alcohol and drug dependency as well as many other forms of mental illness. I once found myself sectioned alongside a man who held a senior post in the local Primary Care Trust. He had suffered the death of a newborn baby and it had triggered manic depression and we spent quite a long time discussing the problems we faced in the mental health unit. I have often wondered if he returned to work and if so if his experience has made any impact on the way patients are treated!

One of the many things I have found about being in a mental health unit is there is a sense of camaraderie. It is a great leveller: most patients are keen to help in any way they can, be it by lending someone money for a much-needed phone call or just by listening to problems, and actually I have learned that this mirrors life. If you have a problem and you ask people for help, most will not refuse.

3. Motherhood and the birth of "Double Trouble"

Almost ten years before the birth of my twins I had been told that I would "almost certainly not be able to have children without medical intervention" so you can imagine my delight when I became pregnant without entering a scientific circus involving IVF or any other medical procedure. This joy was more than doubled when I discovered at 12 weeks that I was carrying twins. I don't know why but I had always wanted two children – I had never thought about having an only child which in the event was just as well!

My pregnancy went very smoothly and I carried on working until October when I could no longer fit behind the wheel of my car! I joined the East Herts Twins Club and made a number of good friends and even managed to keep swimming until December 15! Maybe things were just going too well!

On Friday 15 I had a check up and concern was expressed about the smaller twin. I was admitted for monitoring on the afternoon of December 17 and, having just had my tea, all hell broke lose!

The following are extracts from a diary I kept at the time.
Sunday December 17 1989
The registrar was adamant: "I want them out now!"
Something was wrong, radically wrong, only one twin's heartbeat could be found. All hell broke lose. My husband was banished and I was being "attacked". Nurses were everywhere. Needles were going in my arm, blood seemed to be spewing everywhere...the drip failed to go in properly. I was manhandled into an

operating gown, given a revolting anti-emetic to drink and asked to sign a consent form. I was shaking from head to foot. The nurses ran down the corridor with the bed and we went to the theatre in a lift...the anaesthetist seemed to be strangling me as he explained "it is necessary to pinch the cartilage in your wind pipe to stop you choking on any vomit because you've only just eaten, it won't actually hurt but I believe it is an unpleasant sensation"...

What an understatement. I thought I had been choked to death and even now I hate anyone touching my throat. Each time I have experienced a manic episode since, one of my delusions is that I am being choked.

So a huge crisis, a big drama, then at 9.43 and 9.45pm two tiny, perfect, beautiful baby girls. They were three weeks premature and both quite poorly. They had to stay in special care, two floors below me, for five days but I was nursed intensively for two weeks before I was allowed home.

Tuesday December 19 1989
As I lay paralysed, unable to move a single limb, my mind began to move at speed – I would never be able to look after my twin daughters, my life was at an end, would my babies survive? I must get help.
I was in a side ward on my own. I shouted. No one could hear. Was my voice paralysed too? No, of course not, I could hear myself speak, shout; someone must hear. I lay motionless looking at the emergency cord...it was 2 o'clock in the morning, surely I would be found soon...
"It is post-operative shock" the doctor said reassuringly. I will just lift your head and sensation will return" and so it did. The relief was incredible. When I lay down, sleep eluded me.

I now believe this was almost certainly the onset of my "double trouble" or manic illness. This is partially because of the vivid and intense recollection I have of this period in my life. In my experience each of my manic episodes has been very vivid and etched indelibly on my mind. I was once told by a health professional that "you won't remember any of this when you are better", but that is blatantly not true in my case.

There were some lighter moments. Father Christmas came to me, three times, as well as Jenny and Helen in special care. He brought them some little pink teddies and some clothes knitted especially for premature babies. When he came to me on Christmas morning I was in a very undignified state, having my abdomen examined by a doctor. What he saw gave him such a shock that his beard dropped off on the bed! The doctor passed it back to him, grinning all over his face and said "You might be needing this!"

Left: Father Christmas, (student nurse Adrian Sweeney) whose beard fell off onto my bed!

Just after Christmas I suffered a massive haematoma from my abdomen, which is a haemorrhage through the skin. This happened while I was in the shower and I swung from the emergency cord like a bellringer! Nurses came rushing from all directions and carried me back to bed. It was actually a very serious, potentially life threatening event, but while a screen was erected over my chest, a nurse talked calmly to me and asked if she could get me anything. Much to her surprise, I requested a towel and a hairdryer! I have always hated dripping hair, so she set about drying my hair. It cannot be everyone who, when bleeding profusely, decides they want a blow dry! Years later I was told that this massive loss of blood could actually have triggered my manic depression but I will never know if it did.

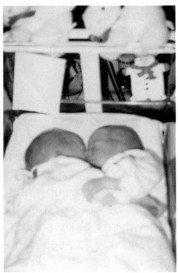

Left: Right at the start of my illness: the first portrait of my new family on 26 December 1989. Photograph courtesy of Dick Smith.
Right: The first I remember of Jenny and Helen snuggled up together in a special care cot looking just as if they are kissing.

From then onwards life was a blur. I could not/dare not rest. I had two precious daughters to look after but I was too ill to be with them so I lay awake planning ahead. I wrote thank you letters and birth announcements...I made lists...I kept a diary...I did everything I could think of to take my mind off the sense of loss. The other new mothers had their babies. I had limited access to mine: all I had was a table over my bed, a pen and paper!

I remember the first time I saw them snuggled up together in a cot, they looked so tiny and fragile but just as if they were kissing! Suddenly I noticed they had names: Jennifer Mary and Helen Margaret – apparently, much to my husband's surprise, I had named them while I was still under the effects of the anaesthetic!

Having said that, having my beautiful, tiny, fragile daughters gave me a reason to live and was a major factor when, several months later, I was contemplating ending it all.

Although I didn't realise it then, by providing myself with an external focus (my babies) I focussed more positively on myself. (Finding an external focus has been something I have done a great deal since to help me through my most difficult times). I knew then that I could not let them grow up without a mother – even if I was going to be the worst mother in the world. Eventually I made myself believe that I now had "a belt" in my husband and "braces" in my daughters and they would keep me afloat through all the very difficult times which lay ahead.

I found it very hard when I did come home to let other people help me to look after them, but I knew I was still too ill to do it alone. One bonus was that my husband, my parents and my mother-in-law forged a very strong bond with them early on and they have always been very close to their dad and their grandparents. However, after my hospitalisation, when they were 13 months old, it became obvious that our family could no longer cope alone and we employed a qualified nanny who came daily and who was a great friend and support to me as well as the girls.

It was the last thing I had ever wanted to do to employ someone to look after my children and it was very hard to find the right person, but we were very lucky and almost 16 years later we still keep in touch with her. However, at the time, I felt that that decision was almost quitting motherhood and it made a very big impact on me and my self-confidence.

I have often been asked about the difficulties surrounding their birth and whether I had ever considered suing the hospital. My attitude is that mistakes were made, but because they became fine, healthy children, my own suffering has been tolerable. Had they not both survived, or had one of them suffered brain damage then the story might be very different!

Leaving hospital on 30 December 1989, eleven days after what I believe was the onset of my "double trouble".

4. Rock bottom – life in a psychiatric unit

Life was a rollercoaster from December to June when the girls were Christened. Because of the drugs I was taking I had to give up breastfeeding (which was about the only bit of motherhood left to me) and this caused me great distress. The girls took to bottles and dummies readily and I had always hated dummies so I felt that I was the biggest failure in the world. Our next door neighbour, a wonderful elderly lady suffering from cancer, who had lived to see our twins, died at the end of January and my back deteriorated badly in March.

Through most of 1990 I hovered precariously on the brink of depression. December was a terrible month. The girls and I all had chest infections and diarrhoea. "My little one" developed an ear infection on the eve of her first birthday and screamed all night. I greeted their birthday with a mixture of horror and delight and the Christmas which followed was actually worse for me than the one I had spent in hospital after their birth!

I spent four days of hell in January 1991 in a psychiatric unit, sectioned. I can recall little about this except that in my desperation I banged my head on the floor and broke my glasses!

Jenny (left) and Helen around the time I was sectioned for the first time. Being away from them, when they were so adorable, contributed to my "hell".

Another clear recollection which shows how strangely my mind was working is that I recall all the toilet roll holders on the ward had the name "Scott" on them! This may seem insignificant to you, as a reader, but to me at the time it was strangely significant. Eric Scott, was the editor who trained me to become an editor and who is still (aged 86) a very good friend.

Before I was hospitalised, I had been trying to contact him and when I couldn't, I assumed he had died and I started to write his obituary as follows:
"Eric Vernon Scott, one of a long line of Great Scotts has finally given up the ghost! His journalistic career led him to be the founder executive and news editor of the Deccan Herald and founder of Egon Publishers…a staunch Roman Catholic, Eric faithfully edited "Contact" on behalf of the Roman Catholic community in Britain…"
At his point I decided I could not carry on and abandoned it, just as well really! I hope this illustrates how bizarrely the human mind works when it is manic.

My experiences have given me an innate fear of hospitals, doctors and drugs. In 2003 I had to go into hospital for an operation and I was absolutely terrified. I had to take sedatives so that I could be admitted and in 2004 I had to have a gastroscopy, where a camera is passed through your mouth and into the stomach, and I had to take sedatives before that too! My idea of hell on earth is being locked up in a psychiatric unit with no pen, no paper, no computer and no urge to function.

I hated everything about the unit. I hated the fact I was locked away from all I was living for; I hated the constant TV (especially the Gulf War) which seemed to be symbolic of the way I was being bombarded and held hostage. I hated being made to use the lifts when I was claustrophobic. I hated the food and the company. I hated the boredom and the lack of fresh air and exercise and I hated the staff who seemed to behave like power-mad prison warders rather than compassionate human beings. Some were kind and sympathetic but I felt victimised and oppressed. Human rights? It seemed to me psychiatric patients had none! Dignity and tender loving care were certainly not in evidence.

In fact, when I am in a psychiatric unit I do not even have the will to survive. About all I am left with is a strong spiritual conviction that somewhere in all this there must be a purpose. Perhaps it is that, through my suffering, and my ability to communicate, I can help others and I hope that by writing this I can do just that.

Although I had been discharged from the section, I was not discharged from the psychiatric unit until March 18 which, to date, has been my longest stay. The fact that I came out at all means that something must have improved while I was in there but I have no idea what! Being discharged gave me a little hope and I remember thinking I can live in hope and with hope and determination all things are possible.

When I left the unit I wrote the following:
"The lift door shut and that was that. I was terrified. I've always hated lifts. This was it, a vacuum to end all vacuums. Part of me knew I would never escape and now, eighteen months later, part of me is still struggling desperately to be free.

I know beyond the doors there is happiness. I know beyond the doors there is life others enjoy. My beautiful

*twin daughters, now eighteen months old, my loving
husband, my home, my friends, my family – but I am a
prisoner held hostage in a lift. The doors are transparent,
I can see the joys of life but I cannot take part.
Sometimes the cruel devil which holds the keys to the lift
presses the button and I go down. Then I panic: I can
see blackness, illness, horror and worst of all I am alone.
No one can reach me down there, try as they might. Yet
gradually, as I endure the darkness, imperceptibly, it
lightens again and I rise to my old level.*

*Just occasionally the lift goes up and I am full of energy
and fun and have an incredible zest for life but then the
lift operator opens the doors and I find myself in hospital
being sedated. It seems there is no ground floor where
the door can open, just a basement or the top floor.*

*I face an uncertain future. We now employ a nanny to
look after our children. I was a journalist and editor and
now I have to face the fact that I may never work again. I
do nothing most of the time except sit in the lift waiting
for the doors to open. I take tablets daily and I cry a lot. I
weep for what I have lost; I weep for what I am missing
with my children; and I weep for the future I cannot face.*

*I have to come to terms with mental illness – "It takes
time", the doctors say, "it is something you will come
through" but when and how they cannot say. They
expect a low after a high. I used to take level for granted,
now I question everything. In the lift nothing is certain; I
have no control, all I have is staying power and some
days that seems to be at a very low ebb!*

*In Ray Moore's book 'Tomorrow is too Late' he cites a
Tennessee Williams play in which he talks about*

someone plagued by bouts of depression and he apparently uses the imagery of a 'blue devil' perched on their shoulder constantly taunting them with sadness and sorrow. That 'blue devil' is operating my lift. Tennessee Williams said the only way out is to endure it because if you do, sooner or later the devil will tire and go away. He may come back but all you have to do is quietly endure it an hour at a time, a minute at a time.

And that is what I try to do but when my powers of endurance weaken I've taken to writing to try and scare the devil that way. To show him there is something in my life I can still control and to try to show others that they are not alone with their illness, I am with them and so I am afraid are many others but we only have 'one devil' between us – DEPRESSION.

There are people I have met who have conquered depression but it seems it has taken years and that, in itself, seems depressing. They say you emerge from it a stronger, better person – this is encouraging but at the moment it seems to me almost beyond hope that I will ever emerge again."

I know many people have written very powerfully about their illnesses and much of it is worth reading. I just wanted to include this because it shows exactly how my mind was working and I hope that other sufferers or their families might identify with some of it.

Fifteen years later... I am out. I hope to stay out. I try and manage my illness with a combination of drugs, common sense, diet, exercise and an increased awareness of my own need to relax and to be stimulated. I have regular blood tests and monthly

check-ups with my GP and I do voluntary work two days
a week.

As for when I emerged, I can't really say. It was very
gradual and it took enormous tenacity. I am not known
for giving in easily and I have always hated being
beaten, which I guess is why I am where I am now!

5. Struggling to stay afloat – "you don't look like a psychiatric patient"!

Between 1990 and 1994 I struggled to stay afloat. I tried to look after my daughters and I loved watching them grow into little people with personalities. I tried to look after myself but I remember thinking that nothing was easy. One thing I did learn was that people are always willing to help. If I needed a lift somewhere or I needed someone to take my daughters somewhere help was always at hand, I only had to ask (that was a difficult lesson to learn!).

I learned too that illness is a great leveller. I had a very good friend who, at that time, had just been diagnosed with breast cancer. There were things she could do and things I could do and we helped each other. Our illnesses were vastly different but our needs (she had a four year old and a two year old) were often similar. Between us we had lots of friends who pitched in and helped and being able to share our ups and downs was really helpful to me.
I remember feeling deeply uncertain. If I felt good I was worried I was going manic, if I felt down I feared depression, but I took comfort from the people who, when told about my illness, said, "you don't look like a psychiatric patient!"

A rare picture of my husband and me. (I hate being photographed!) Do I look like a psychiatric patient? Photograph by Peter Ruffles.

I asked myself then, and I have often asked myself since, what a "psychiatric patient" looks like. Someone helpfully told me that psychiatric patients wear slippers out of doors (well, I do that quite a bit!) but in my experience people suffering from mental illness come from all walks of life. I have met members of the clergy, doctors, academics, tv repair men, dinner ladies and numerous others whose background I haven't even known.

My point is that mental illness, like any other illness, can afflict anyone and although there may be "tell tale signs" which largely happen as side effects to the drugs (such as rocking back and forwards or shaking uncontrollably) there is no such thing as looking like a "psychiatric patient".

"Psychiatric patients" are people with an illness which happens to affect them mentally. They are often more scared of themselves than likely to harm anyone. The nature of mental illness is such that it cannot easily be understood by the sufferer or others and the media seem to delight in labelling people "a danger to the public" when they are mentally ill. This leads to a disproportionate fear of people with mental illness and tends to make them feel even more isolated. I am certain statistics show that more people are killed or injured by cars on the road, drunks on a Friday night and people taking illegal drugs than by people suffering from severe mental illness but human nature and the media seem to be happier to accept the first three groups rather than the last.

Looking back I think this was a period when I tried to come to terms with living with my illness, living with this "psychiatric patient label", and began to learn to "hold my head above the water" and get on with life. I came off lithium carbonate on the advice of my GP and I *seemed* to be relatively stable. I know I did a lot of reflecting on what might have been and I dabbled in some freelance work. My father was ill and was facing major heart surgery; my husband was due to go to France on a business trip and then the IRA exploded a bomb at the end of my parents' road on the railway line in Old Stevenage. It might have been exploded in my head because on August 2 (my niece's 5th birthday) I was re-admitted to the psychiatric unit.

On this occasion I walked miles round Old Stevenage and went on a shopping spree, buying presents for everyone, because I had such a sense of failure and guilt. I now know that wild shopping sprees are often part of manic illness. Stephen Fry recently admitted that during a manic episode when he was 17 "I bought ridiculous suits with stiff collars and silk ties from the 1920s, and would go to the Savoy and Ritz and drink cocktails".

I was deluded and manic again. I was bitterly disappointed and I was back to square one...I felt helpless, hopeless and furious when I realised I was going to be sectioned again. I felt a burden to my family. I was a further worry to my parents; my husband missed his trip to France and I felt my world had collapsed.

In desperation, I grabbed a fire extinguisher from the wall at the entrance to the unit and let it off at the policemen who were trying to get me admitted. (This is the only "dangerous" thing I have ever done during my illness and I feel ashamed to mention it, but I think it is important because I felt so trapped and desperate.) Sending police officers and paramedics along with social workers and other members of the "crash team" seems to be a disproportionate response to a middle-aged woman who has lost the plot and is "throwing a wobbly" because she can't handle the stress of life. Calm, gentle persuasion and perhaps a little tea and sympathy (with maybe a Mars bar) would certainly make me feel more ready to co-operate and go to hospital!

When you are confused, scared and desperate being confronted by "the cavalry" is enough to drive you insane! I have often wondered if, when I discharged the extinguisher, I looked like a "psychiatric patient" or just a desperate woman. I know which I felt!

6. The death of my father - another spell in hell

My father, very at home with a book, a pint of beer and a pipe! He contributed a unique blend of mild eccentricity, wonderful sense of humour, pragmatism and common sense to my life which has helped me come to terms with my illness. Photograph by Barry Pywell.

My father's death was sudden. He had been unwell with heart problems for more than ten years. He had survived major heart surgery in December 1994 but during 1995 he did not improve as he hoped he would. At the beginning of October his legs began to swell and he was taken into hospital and was waiting to be transferred to Harefield when he died.

Looking back to December 1994, when we thought he was going to die, during surgery, is really rather amusing. My husband and I took him to Harefield and he said he wanted a word with me. Naturally I thought this would be a somewhat sad moment but all he said was "I know if I don't survive you will look after your mum, but please make sure she buys a reliable car and a decent lawn mower!" So that was it. My father had given me his last wishes!

My father was a very pragmatic and slightly eccentric man. From very young I can remember him telling us that there were "only two certainties in life, death and the tax man and if you've paid your taxes you have nothing to fear in life"!

His operation was carried out on December 2 and we had been told it could take five days for him to come round properly, so when, on December 3, my sister received a call from Harefield, she feared the worst. However, the caller said "Your father is insisting on speaking to you" and to her amazement he came on the line to wish her a very happy birthday and a very happy day it was for us all! He had said he would ring her on her birthday but none of us believed he would. To which he replied "O ye of little faith!" Apparently when he came round from the anaesthetic, the first question he asked was what date it was, and then he started asking to ring my sister. At first the staff thought he was under the influence of the drugs but when he persisted they relented. He was always a man of his word.

By October 1995 it was clear he was frustrated by his lack of improvement and his deteriorating health was getting him down. He had lost much of his will to live but he was convinced there was nothing wrong with him that Professor Yacoub could not fix. Having said that I do recall him saying he felt that not only had he passed his "Best Before Date" but he feared he might be past his "Sell By Date" so it was a much less positive man who went into the Lister Hospital to wait for a bed in Harefield.

Once in hospital, his spirit was broken. Almost three weeks later he was a desperate man. I asked him what I could do for him and he said "get me out of here!" I protested but he said no, find a wheelchair, get me a pint of beer and a cigarette, and take me outside for some fresh air. This desperation struck a chord with me and so on Thursday 19 October, I did just that. He was a changed man.

Fresh air, a pint of beer and a cigarette, restored his spirit. We sat for almost an hour in the late sunshine chatting and watching the world go by…he was his old self. We talked about me buying a new car and I chose the model and the colour with his help…the next day my mother got a phone call to say he was critically ill. They might be able to save his life by amputating his legs but otherwise he would have to be put on life support. We knew he would not want the former so we opted for the latter but were told he was not expected to last the weekend. He died early in the morning of Sunday 22 October.

I was initially relieved. I was pleased he wasn't suffering and I was pleased that we had enjoyed such a lovely interlude in the fresh air. I knew too well how awful being stuck in hospital felt. I knew he had lost much of the quality of life he had enjoyed and I knew he would be happy to finally meet his maker. What I didn't know was how we would all cope without him.

My daughters (then aged 4) took his death in their stride. Jenny made a very long paper ladder so that he could climb up to heaven while Helen took comfort from the fact that there was still a Lancaster flying, so that Grandad could go to heaven in it! (He had worked on Lancaster's during WW2, as an engineer, and always said they were his first love, my mother his second!)

It was a difficult time but I seemed to be coping and then my mother was taken ill and rushed into hospital with a blocked bowel. She was less than 8 hours from death when they operated and suddenly I was back in the hell of the psychiatric unit…

I felt guilty for leaving my sister to look after my mother, albeit that she was still in hospital. Locked up without the rest of my family I missed my father even more, and then there was the realisation that this was likely to occur again and again at critical points in my life.

Despair was persistent. I lay on the floor and begged to die and then the staff gave me an injection and I felt giddy and sick.

I discussed suicide with another patient who eventually jumped under a train. Her death hit me hard. Life seemed very cruel indeed…but I knew I could not end it all. Two other women sectioned with me, also went on to commit suicide but I remained convinced that my life was not mine to end. My life belonged to my family, especially my daughters, and I knew I owed it to them to get better but how? I also felt a deep underlying conviction, based on my faith, that suicide was not an option for me even though death held tremendous appeal.

When I came out of hospital I was not allowed to drive and I also found the law had changed and DVLA and the insurance companies needed to know about any long term medication you were taking. This meant that I didn't end up buying the new car my father and I had discussed for another 14 months, but, when I did, I managed to get the exact model and colour we had discussed and I loved it.

Since then, I have found being discharged from hospital very difficult because, after being sectioned, I have not been allowed to drive and I have to renew my licence more frequently (currently every 2 years). Given that I usually feel very weak and exhausted when I come home and that my confidence and self-esteem are at rock bottom, I am not in a good position to do a lot of walking or to tackle public transport. The latter is something I intend to tackle while I am well so that it is less daunting when I am ill.

I always feel that being without my car is like a bereavement and a punishment as it leaves me feeling very isolated and helpless.

7. Paralysed by fear and frustration, prone to panic attacks

I have very little recollection of this traumatic time in 1995. I know people say that the human memory is selective and only recalls the good bits but this was a really dreadful time and I recall almost nothing. Unlike during my manic episodes, I was so frightened I didn't even keep a diary.

I do know that there was a race on between my mother and me as to who would get out of hospital first. I desperately wanted to visit her and she was equally determined to come and see me. In the event within 24 hours of my release, my sister and I were arranging for her to move into a nursing home temporarily. She was still very poorly but being discharged from hospital and we knew that we could not look after her. She spent one of the worst weeks of her life in the home, surrounded by senile dementia patients, before her brother and sister-in-law took her home with them for some tender loving care. They came and picked me up, because once again I could not drive, and we finally managed to spend some time together which was mutually beneficial.

My mother's close shave with death made me value her even more and gradually together we looked at ways to face the future. At Easter 1996 she went "back to work" volunteering at her local hospice shop and in October 1996, following the death of my friend, in August, with breast cancer, I joined the Hertfordshire Fundraising Office of Marie Curie Cancer Care as a volunteer one day a week handling local publicity and helping organise fundraising events.

My sister, my mother and me (left to right) on my mother's 70th birthday, just five months after my father died. My mother had just started volunteer work and was a great inspiration to me. Photograph by Barry Pywell.

My mother often helped me – especially on "Daffodil Day" when we collected together all day and she would then count the money with my husband. The team we organised to do the street collections regularly raised around £1,000 a day in exchange for the synthetic daffodils we offered in return for a donation. We were a small part of a national day raising awareness of the Marie Curie nurses and much needed funds for their home nursing service.

The daffodil was chosen because it is an international symbol of hope and somehow it gave us hope too. She and I had a lot of fun thinking of ways to raise money and she helped me organise a local Barn Dance to celebrate the 50th anniversary of the Marie Curie Cancer Care charity. We made a good team and together we decided we had become "do-gooders", a breed my father would often mock! We spoke almost every day and together we got on with our lives, something that we knew my father was adamant we should do. By the way, she bought a new car three weeks before he went into hospital and a new lawnmower while he was in, so I pointed out that she had fulfilled his last wishes with time to spare!

When I read that back, it sounds easy, but believe me overcoming the feelings of fear and frustration and all the panic attacks was not as easy as it sounds. I also had the added fear of losing my mother which would haunt me for another nine years but I started swimming regularly again to try and get fit and lose some weight and while the exercise definitely helped me mentally it took enormous courage. Sometimes I would be half way through a length and begin to panic and fear I would drown. As a result of this, I found a pool where I could stay in my depth and I would stop and reassure myself that I was OK and carry on. With hindsight, this was not very sensible, I should have gone with someone or told the lifeguards, but I survived anyway.

I regained a lot of confidence from organising public relations events. I proved I could still produce "column inches" and raise the profile of an organisation whose nurses had cared for my friend. I knew she would be pleased that I was not sitting at home moping. We had discussed returning to work and while she was certain she never would, I **doubted** that I ever would but she urged me to try and by volunteering I had. I had found a niche for myself and I felt it would benefit others in her situation. Because of her young family, she chose to be nursed at home so that she could be with them and I knew that this was something she dearly wanted. (I also knew it was something I would have wanted too in her situation). So somehow life had a purpose beyond survival and it began to feel almost worth living again. When you talk to other volunteers, they often have a need to work but volunteering gives them a bit more flexibility and it is symbiotic. The more you give, the more satisfaction you receive.

Panic attacks affect many people, lots of whom do not have mental illness. They are very frightening and debilitating and I have to say I have never found any one solution to them. Sometimes deep "diaphragmatic breathing" helps. Sometimes Bach's Rescue Remedy can stave off an attack and sometimes positive thinking, inhaling lavender and listening to music works for me. Although I have had them during the day, most of mine have been at night, so I now keep all my remedies by my bed!

I rarely have really bad attacks these days. I have now begun to recognise when they are likely to happen. When I am very tired, very stressed and then usually when I try and relax and go to sleep. I used to have attacks which lasted all night where I would be shaking all the time and urinating frequently. I have vomited and suffered diarrhoea too but if I fear I am heading that way now I book a massage or, as a last resort, take 10mg of Temazepam before bed. I know people who have thought they were having a heart attack during a panic attack and certainly my heart pounds and races. However, a good night's sleep always makes me feel much better. If I have to take three consecutive doses of Temazepam I ring my GP and discuss the problems with him.

8. Music and lyrics – comfort and escapism

Long before I was ill, my father used to joke about living with three women and say the trouble was we didn't ever "switch off and let the set cool down". This was usually in response to one of us complaining that he had dozed off in the chair while watching TV and/or reading the newspaper! He maintained the human brain was just like a TV set, it needed to be switched off and allowed to cool down several times a day but he reckoned that it was mainly only men who had perfected the technique. The longer I live the more I am sure he was right!

However since the onset of my illness, those words have often come back to haunt me, especially when I have been manic or depressed. How I would love to have control of a switch to just stop all those thoughts whirling around in my head. When I am manic it is exhausting and when I am depressed I am just swamped by their negativity. Recently, while I was on the Expert Patients Programme, for people suffering from long-term illness, I started practising positive thinking and positive self-talk. After the first two days I felt thoroughly depressed because I realised just how negative I had become! However, I persevered, and now I am more positive than I have been for a long time. Whether I could manage to do it when I am depressed I don't know, but I would certainly try.

When my illness began my husband had bought me the double cassette of the musical "Love Changes Everything". He bought it for me to listen to while I was in labour, but as I never went into labour I listened to it by way of escapism from my health problems and the hospital generally. When I shut my eyes I could visualise

Michael Ball on stage in the show which I had seen when I was seven months pregnant. I took great comfort from the lyrics and I loved his voice and it evoked happy memories so I listened to it as much as I could and it almost became my "switch".

Since then I have regularly used music as a retreat. Once I have recovered from the horror of realising that I only have what I am standing up in when I arrive at hospital, I try and make sure I have got plenty of Michael Ball CDs and spare batteries for my personal CD player. It is interesting how important lyrics become when you are detached from reality. I have homed in on certain music, especially by Michael Ball, because of the sentiment and the emotions. I have since been to two more of his concerts and I can visualise his cheerful face and his impish laugh more readily. For some reason it seems to help. One of my favourite "comfort zones" is to lie in a hot bath, or just on my bed, and listen to music. I often joke that I am just going for a lie down with Michael Ball and I do not want to be disturbed. I am sure he would appreciate the joke!

In the last five years I have also begun silk painting which is a wonderfully mind-absorbing hobby and one which you can do while listening to music. I find that if I make silk painted cards there is the added bonus in that other people are really thrilled to receive them. I have also painted scarves and small pictures and I find that watching the paint spread across the silk calms and absorbs my mind in a very gentle and satisfying way. When I was working at a drop-in centre for people with severe mental illness, I introduced silk painting and it was very popular. Not only did the members find it

relaxing but they also took great satisfaction from their finished items.

Sadly, silk painting has not been available in any of the mental health units that I have stayed in, but, interestingly, it is available to the patients at the hospice where I work as a volunteer and it is a very popular occupation. Although it is a relatively expensive hobby, at the hospice we find the patients buy the finished items and we recoup most of the cost.

I have often thought that instead of being sectioned in a psychiatric unit, I would recover more quickly if I were sent to a health farm where I could get exercise, be pampered, be fed well and take part in relaxation classes as well as being able to swim, have a massage, lounge in a whirlpool or steam room and generally chill out! I have found that sitting in a steam room or a whirlpool also helps me "switch off".

Certainly it would be more pleasant, less intimidating and more relaxing than being locked in a unit where alarms constantly sound and I feel completely unable to relax even with my music. (In fact, I have been criticised by staff for "cutting myself off" from life on the unit by listening to music all the time!")

Perhaps this is a just a female dream, but it seems that if I were most men, a TV, a newspaper and a cup of tea (or even a pint of beer) might be all that was required to achieve that blissful state of escapism when the brain is "switched off" and "the set" has a chance to cool down.

9. Doctors, consultants and alternative therapists

Anyone living with a long term medical condition will know that visiting doctors and consultants becomes a way of life. It is therefore helpful if you can build a good relationship with at least some of them. Somebody likened these relationships to marriage, in that they will involve give and take on both sides. Although I have always managed to get on very well with almost all the GPs I have seen, I have found hospitals and consultants, and especially their teams, very frustrating and I know I am not alone in this.

With a condition such as manic depression, continuity is very valuable and although consultants don't change very frequently their housemen and registrars do. This means that there is very little chance of seeing the same person more than twice and consequently there is a feeling of taking two steps forward and three back on almost every visit. If the doctor has no real idea of what to expect when you are well, how can he judge your behaviour when you are ill?
I remember one house doctor saying to me "You are speaking a lot and very fast, do you think you might be slightly manic?" Now everyone who knows me, would tell you I tend to talk: a) a lot and b) quite fast all the time. So when confronted by a doctor who says "Can you tell me a bit about yourself?" and I know I have to précis about 10 years medical history into ten minutes, I know I will speak even faster! I have to say I felt sorry for him but even sorrier for myself!

I have now reached a stage, through medication and self-management, where I have regular (monthly) check-ups with my own GP and have been discharged from the consultant and his team, which is working very well for me.

I am very fortunate in that my own GP has an excellent philosophy – one I'm sure most doctors have when they start practising – that he would rather spend 5 minutes making sure I'm staying well, than half a day, or more, trying to find a hospital bed so that I can be sectioned in a mental health unit. He has been practising over 30 years and I guess he is one in a million, but I'm sure there are others who operate with the same helpful holistic approach. Although I would not say our relationship is in any way like a marriage, interestingly he is very similar in temperament to my husband and he has a very similar sense of humour to his, which helps me greatly. I have to say, without his input, I very much doubt whether I would be writing this book at all.

Having said that I have been very lucky with my GP; I have also found some excellent alternative therapists. Although my GP has suggested there is little evidence to show they will help, I have tried acupuncture, counselling, aromatherapy, reflexology, the Bowen Technique, Indian Head massage and massage for therapy and I know I have benefited from them all in some way or another. When my GP suggests I must be mad to spend money on such therapies I reply "Yes, and I've been certified to prove it!" At least he and I have established a rapport which allows my sense of humour and his sense of incredulity to flourish side by side! Unfortunately no one has ever offered me an alternative therapy on the NHS but my family has borne all the cost, believing that health is more important than wealth.

It always seems odd to me that if there is, say, a sudden death in a school, a team of counsellors is sent in. In all my stays in mental health units the only therapy I have been offered is art therapy and then only one session. Given that two of my stays were the direct result of the death of a parent, why did nobody even mention bereavement counselling? Sadly the NHS does not seem to see the value of alternative therapy in mental health and, in my personal experience, it has been extremely beneficial.

My advice to anyone suffering from manic depression is not to give up. Keep taking the medication but try as many alternative therapies as you can. If something works stick with it. I know people who have found yoga very helpful and others who find meditation and Reiki helpful.

Personally I find prayer useful and I have taken great comfort from the healing services run, once a month, in my local Church of England church, where hands are placed on my head while the vicar offers a prayer asking for, among other things, "healing and light".

I cannot pretend I have felt a sudden dramatic improvement and often I have felt desperate for a miracle, but I have found it very comforting to be treated in this holistic way by someone who treats me as a person with an illness, rather than locking me up like a dangerous criminal. I have discovered that quite a number of sufferers from manic depression have a strong faith, and I will discuss the role of religion in more detail later.

I would also say that whether you have faith or none, it is important to build good relations with doctors, consultants, therapists and any professional, such as a priest, who can be called upon when you are desperate. I look on a number of close friends, with a variety of backgrounds, as valuable DIY tools. Everyone has problems and many will be there for you when you need them. I try and look on my GP more as a friend – I also know someone who is a trained counsellor and I know two retired priests – who will always listen. There is always someone – The Samaritans for instance - who will be there for you but you do have to ask and it is not always easy to recognise that you need help, let alone ask for it!

NB. I am very well aware that this book does not deal with the medical issues and ethical problems associated with treating manic depression which can be very difficult. Clearly they would need to come from a medical professional, such as my GP.

10. Pushing back the boundaries: assessing my achievements

I have talked about how volunteering helped me to move on in life. It gave me a purpose and a feeling of professional fulfilment. The latter was something I never expected to find again after the onset of my illness. I recently reviewed my CV and since the onset of my illness in 1989 I have added the following:

March 2005 – present	**Day Hospice Administrator** (2-days a week voluntary job share).
June 2005 – November 2005	**Community Support Worker with Rethink at the Connect 3 Friendship club** Charity for people with severe mental illness (one day a week)
July 2004 – January 2005	**Certificate in Interpersonal Skills for Volunteers (Distinction) University of Wales, Lampeter Organiser of Hertford's second Christmas Tree Festival**
April 2003 – June 2004	**Isabel Hospice Volunteer** (one half day a week) **Freelance writing for Hertfordshire Life (paid)**
1999 – 2003	**St. Andrew's Church, Hertford Parish Administrator (paid)**
1996 – 2002	**Marie Curie Cancer Care Hertfordshire Fundraising Office Voluntary Assistant** (one day a week) **Total involvement with the charity over 6 years helped raise over £30,000**

When you realise that only the freelance writing, the post of parish administrator and the work for Connect 3 were paid work it shows what you can achieve through volunteering. When I say that, I don't mean what you can achieve for the charity, but how you can rebuild your skills, confidence and self-esteem.

I remember answering the advert for volunteers for the Marie Curie Fundraising office with a mixture of hope and trepidation. It was almost a year since my father had died, and just over two months since I had lost my friend to cancer and I felt compelled to do something. My "interview" was very relaxed and the fundraiser, who, although retired, has remained a good friend, did not recoil in horror when I mentioned my illness. She was more interested in how she could best utilize my skills and this felt like a real breakthrough for me.

We agreed that I would go into the offices, one day a week, and do everything from filing and making tea to writing local press releases, and soon I found myself doing all kinds of things. I organized a Golf Day in conjunction with our local newspaper and a Barn Dance to celebrate the charity's 50th anniversary. I was back in the real world helping others and I began to look forward to my Thursdays!

Although I started a paid job, one day a week, as Parish Administrator, in 2003, I maintained some contact with Marie Curie and continued to organize collections for them on Daffodil Day until 2002. Once the original fundraiser retired and the office moved, I decided it was time for me to move on too.

Joining Isabel Hospice as a volunteer was an easier step although it involved an induction course and learning more new skills. I have worked on reception in the Day Hospice as well as in the Volunteers office, helping to co-ordinate their work, and currently I "job share" two days a week with the administrator at the Day Hospice. I produce correspondence, statistics and rotas as well as doing filing, photocopying and making phone calls and I feel very much appreciated and part of a team doing something very worthwhile.

Never, in my wildest dreams could I have thought, in 1990, when I was so ill physically and mentally that in 16 years my CV would read like that. I mean me, help raise over £30,000, when I was a gibbering wreck with no will to go on! I would have sworn I would never be useful again – let alone use my talents to such effect!

But there you are, I did it and I am sure I will go on achieving things. It didn't all happen over night. I have gradually pushed back the boundaries of my comfort zone.

Instead of staying in bed paralysed by the fear and frustration of my illness, I started making a point of getting washed and dressed before lunch. Then I started dressing smartly instead of slopping around in track suits and I started wearing make up to go out – like I used to do for work. It was all little tiny steps. Some days I failed. Some days I went back to bed and cried, but in time getting up and dressed became the norm. As soon as someone said "I like your blouse" "that's a nice necklace" or "that dress looks good on you" I started to be able to hide my feelings behind my appearance. I wore a mask of coping and doing so enabled me to cope better with everyday chores.

This lesson in life was sparked when I was in my teens and I was very upset having split up from a boyfriend. My father said "Come on, stop crying, put on a face and we'll go out. If you can put on a face you can do anything." I was puzzled and asked him what he meant and he said "When I joined the RAF during the war I knew I had to be able to kill someone if necessary and I was terrified. So one day I put on my uniform and went out onto the Sussex Downs. I took my rifle and I shot a fox. I hated killing it but I had proved to myself that by putting on that uniform, I could kill." So, he said if you put on some smart clothes and some make-up you can create a mask of coping with your heartbreak. I did, and I've done it many times since.

The strategy had lain largely dormant for years but now the less I want to do something, the longer I take to get ready and ensure that the mask hides my fear.
For my father's funeral, which I was dreading, I bought a whole new outfit and went to the hairdressers to have my hair done. For my mother's funeral, where I actually did a long reading, the day after I left the mental health unit, I wore a new dress and I put on my mother's favourite perfume! If I feel that I look my best, I cope better and it helps me fly in the face of my illness. (I read recently that one of the tell-tale signs of people suffering from severe mental illness is often a loss of appearance and a lack of personal hygiene so I now hang on to mine like grim death!)

When I assess my achievements, which are not earth shattering, I make myself look back at where I started with this illness and where I end up each time I am hospitalized. I know then that I have achieved an enormous amount because each one has involved me pushing thousands of tiny barriers of fear and panic aside – including the fear of failure – I feel a great sense of pride. I am proudest of all that I chose not to lie in bed and give in to all my negativity. I know many people, especially my family and friends, have helped and encouraged me every step of the way, but it was I who **chose** not to become bed-ridden with fear and grief. I really do believe that the only person who can tackle this illness, particularly the depression, successfully is the sufferer.

You can choose to stay locked in the lift, in the basement, or you can start to look for ways to let others know you are stuck and want to get out. Others can try and get you out, but if you don't try really hard you will still be stuck. It will take more energy, physically and mentally, than you think you can muster, but my father was absolutely right:
YOU DO NOT KNOW WHAT YOU CAN DO UNTIL YOU REALLY TRY!
My father was also very fond of saying:
IF AT FIRST YOU DON'T SUCCEED, TRY, TRY AND TRY AGAIN!
And they are probably two of the best pieces of advice I can give anyone who is trying to live successfully with this illness.

11. The role of religion – a test of faith?

When I was researching manic depression on the internet I came across a personal story by James Wooldridge entitled "Living with Manic Depression" in which he says: "Prior to my admission to hospital I was a struggling Christian and at many times I felt my situation was a test of faith. There were times when I could have given up and if it meant the crisis in my mind would stop, I'd have gladly done so. However, giving up was anything but an easy option and anyway, amongst the times of desperation there were also glimpses of a world that was so beautiful and full of love that I often broke down and cried with joy." His story is well worth reading, but this particular extract struck a chord with me and my experiences.

Like James, before my illness began I was a Christian. I have always gone to church, sometimes more regularly than at others, but I had never had a "defining moment" when my faith had been confirmed or denied. I guess I saw my faith as part of me. My parents were both Christians, and my father and his family all had a very strong faith. Sometimes, I almost felt I had "inherited" an element of Christianity which was a privilege and I treasured my faith and it gave me comfort.

On Sunday 17 December 1989, the day my daughters were born, I attended Holy Communion and prayed a very simple, if naive, prayer: "God, if it be your will, let these babies be delivered safely". At that stage I only knew I was going into hospital to be monitored in the evening.

To my amazement 12 hours later they were here! Now, I don't, and never have, seen what happened during and after their birth as an answer to my prayers, but my illness has raised questions about my faith.

As a result of my illness I became friends with a lady in her late 80s (she died aged 97), who had also suffered from manic depression. She very much saw her illness as a test of faith and we discussed this issue a lot. Like me, when she had suffered depression she had felt detached from, and forsaken by, God, but when she was manic she described herself as "flying with God" and I could identify very closely with her experiences too.

In order to try and deal with her "test of faith" she spent about a year living in a convent in Canada. While it obviously didn't cure her illness, it certainly seemed to help her and by the end of her life she had a very strong faith. I took great comfort from her friendship and she regarded me as a "special" friend because we shared so much that we could not hope others would ever understand.

She once told me that when she was too distressed by her illness to do anything else, she recited the Lord's Prayer, over and over, in her head. In his article James Wooldridge refers to: "A massive war between good and evil was being fought between my ears and having been taught that 'The Good Book' was a source of inspiration for many, I turned to it often, sometimes pounding my head with my copy while praying fervently as if my very life depended on it".

In my desperation, I have recited parts of the Communion service and begged for Holy Communion at 3 o'clock in the morning, while locked in psychiatric unit.

I am sure this will sound very odd to many but it seems that manic depression, along with other mental illnesses, often engenders strong religious conflict.

Going back to the issue of "flying with God" when I am manic everything seems to make perfect sense. Life is very vivid and exciting and I feel very much in tune with my faith and very close to God, but when I am then thrown into depression life seems very cruel and the depths of despair conjure up visions of hell – a deep black pit with no obvious means of escape and barely a shred of hope. It is a place where there is no sign of God and yet, oddly, even when I have been in that pit I have refused to contemplate suicide because, among other things, I have said that I believe that my life is not mine to take. It belongs to God.

The fact that I am still here to tell this tale bears testimony to my faith and I am grateful for that.

Thankfully, these two very extreme religious experiences are not a regular occurrence but having experienced them I am left with trying to come to terms with my faith the rest of the time. I recently heard a sermon about Pentecost and the vicar described a sense of comfort and safety at being hidden from sight, when as a young boy, he used to hide in a wardrobe. This was how I felt with my faith before my illness. My faith and I lived together, privately, in a comfort zone which was not greatly challenged, but which I felt no need to challenge. In the sermon he then went on to talk about the power of God going through locked doors.

This made me think that perhaps when I have been in the pit of depression, and I have felt trapped in the lift with no access to the controls, my faith has actually been locked in with me and it is the power of God which has sustained me. Certainly, I don't think I would have accepted that explanation at the time, but looking back, I remember complaining that I felt almost equally trapped by my faith, which would not let me take my own life.

I am now thinking my experience may have been like the "Footprints in the Sand". There were two sets of footprints and when times got tough, there was only one, the walker felt deserted and questioned God, but He simply said "I was there, I carried you".

Equally, when I am manic and everything seems possible, and I feel I have the power to go through locked doors, maybe I am actually experiencing the power of God. The rest of the time I retreat to the comfort of my faith and try not to question it too much.

I also take heart from the fact that whether you are ill or not, faith can't be proved!

12. Starting work again and more volunteering

Following the last chapter, perhaps it is no coincidence that when I returned to some paid work it was for the church! It was, however, not something I did easily. I agreed to take on the hitherto un-charted territory of parish administrator for a trial period of three months to help our erstwhile Rector out. He had known me since just before my daughters were born, and they were now 12. So we were not exactly strangers but having said that, when you come to work very closely with someone, you get to know them very much better.

Revd Graham Edwards, a former Rector of Hertford, St Andrew, who employed me as his first Parish Administrator Photograph by Peter Ruffles.

He was very confident in my abilities, not least because he was not computer literate and I was, but there were many times when I would joke that the computer was the work of the devil designed to drive me to distraction! However, for all my mistakes and heartache with the computer, I gradually began to make the job of parish administrator happen!

I was utterly amazed that so many of my seemingly lost abilities returned. Behind the title of "Parish Administrator" I was no longer simply a manic depressive. I functioned in many ways as professionally as I had done before my illness and the job was very different. There were many times when people complimented me on my diplomacy or tact, my thoughtfulness or my kindness, and I began to realise that they were witnessing aspects of my character which had developed through my own experience of illness. I hope I was never hard-hearted and hurtful to people with health issues, but I realised I had become really interested in people, and their illnesses and problems. Although most of my work was working from home on a computer, I really enjoyed the small amount of work I got involved with especially with the elderly and infirm.

As I have said before, I have always thrived on organisation and although, it was only, in theory, one day a week, being parish administrator did me the power of good. I would slip into the role and my illness would recede. The Rector and I shared a very good sense of humour and the laughter was very healing. I realised that, although I still saw the funny side of things, I rarely laughed – well who does sit at home and laugh when they have a long term illness? I did the job for three and a half years in the end and for the next two years I worked in a voluntary capacity as PA to the Rector until his retirement. I decided to leave to work as a volunteer at my local hospice because I really wanted to explore the people part of my work more. I also felt it would not be good for me to leave when he retired as that would leave a large vacuum for the parish.

Through being parish administrator, not only did I gain a great deal of experience, but I gained the friendship of the Rector and his wife who have come to know me and my family very well. They have been wonderfully supportive of us through some very difficult times and I hope will always keep in touch.

But what does all this say about my illness? I honestly don't think I could have done the job as well before I was ill. I am sure that my illness has given me new dimensions which I was able to use in the role. I have to say I don't think I would even have considered taking a job working closely with a clergyman who was heading for retirement – I often joked "I must be mad to do this, but I have certificates to prove it!" However, I certainly don't regret it. It improved my self-confidence, raised my self-esteem, helped me rediscover my sense of humour and the ability to laugh and therefore helped me to move on from my illness and find other challenges!

13. Moving forward – creating new challenges

If you read my CV, since 1989, in chapter 10 you will see that I undertook all sorts of new challenges as a volunteer working for Marie Curie Cancer Care. I arranged a number of publicity stunts to start with and then moved on to a Golf Day (which took a year and was run in conjunction with our local newspaper). I also organised an anniversary Barn Dance with about 250 people. This was all done with the support and expertise of the fundraiser for Marie Curie Cancer Care in Hertfordshire. I will admit I lost a lot of sleep over all of them and there were times when I wished I'd never started, but looking back now I am glad I rose to those challenges and I really loved the feeling of satisfaction when they were over. They gave me "a natural high" as opposed to a "high" through my manic illness and my involvement with them helped raise over £30,000 in 6 years – this was a tangible achievement.

Prior to my illness I had never thought of myself as a high achiever. I knew I had a tendency towards being a perfectionist and obviously editing and PR required that in no small amount but I just accepted that what I did was very normal and did not really question what made me do it beyond enjoying the writing and finding much of it very interesting. I always felt that I was living in a very "plastic world" where every press reception I attended everyone was "fine" and everything "good" or "fantastic" but I did it.

Since my illness, I feel I have moved into a different, more real, world. My volunteering has bought me into contact with real people with real problems and I have really got to know quite a lot of people.

When I left Marie Curie as a volunteer to work as Parish Administrator, I was keen to remain in contact with them and, in December 2001, the idea of organising a Christmas Tree Festival in our church to raise money for the church and Marie Curie came to me as a way to combine the two. By December 2002, when I had been the organiser of Hertford's first Christmas Tree Festival for a year, it bore fruit and £3,400 was split between the two!
Although I organised it, almost single-handed, I had a fantastic amount of support from friends and family who all pitched in to make it such a success. Despite all the panic attacks and migraines I suffered as a result, the face of one small boy which lit up, when 40 sets of Christmas tree lights came on, will be an abiding memory. The pleasure it gave to so many people made it all worthwhile. I was presented with a "Gold Star" from the Rector and his wife and I received a superb letter of thanks from the Mayor of Hertford which my mother urged me to frame to mark my achievement.

Somehow, I knew it would not end there and in 2004 I organised another Christmas Tree Festival. It raised £3,800 which was split between the church and the Lavender Trust (a breast care charity for young women). However, in June 2004, my mother died suddenly and I had another bout of illness. So although the achievement may have been even greater, it was tinged with a great deal of sadness for me as she was not alive to see it and to share it.
I knew it had to go ahead as my mother always faced

deaths with the attitude that "life must go on" and somehow that determination manifested itself in me… the festival must go on…and it was a legacy I could not ignore.

14. The death of my mother – two more weeks of hell

My mother, though desperately worried about my illness, always believed "life must go on". She always kept busy and never allowed herself to wallow in self-pity – a very valuable lesson. Photograph by Barry Pywell.

Looking back now the death of my mother was strangely similar to the death of my father. She was taken ill on June 19 and died on June 30 – completely unexpectedly.

She stayed with my sister for two days initially when she was ill but then she came to stay with us because my sister had just lost her father-in-law to cancer and she was very busy dealing with the aftermath of that. During her stay, despite having "a stomach bug", she was her usual resilient self and although it was obvious she was very ill, we shared lots of "quality time" together. We laughed a lot and we reminisced and she made light of feeling awful. She even got dressed and came out "window shopping" with me. She sat in the car looking at clothes saying "when I'm feeling better, I'll try that jacket on" such was her fighting spirit! Two days later she collapsed through dehydration and I called an ambulance and she was rushed to hospital. When she first arrived at A & E she was very positive, but once she was admitted, she seemed to go down hill quite fast.

I was studying with the University of Wales at the time for a Certificate in Interpersonal Skills for Volunteers and I was working on the chapter about assertiveness. Mother was adamant I should continue my studies and I found myself putting theory into practice.

No one seemed to know what was wrong with my mother. All the tests showed nothing but she did not improve. She was still being assessed but she seemed to be being treated as if she had dementia. Obviously I was upset and I went and had a cup of tea and shed some tears and then I started to be assertive. I asked to see the nurse in charge and I presented her with a list of questions and one of facts. I demanded that my mother's name be put on the door of her ward and that someone actually consider the facts and answer the questions. The result was quite astonishing.

The sister made me another cup of tea and sat down with me and talked the whole thing through. I made it very clear that without her glasses my mother could not see and without her hearing aid she could not hear! I also pointed out that mother was demanding to know what was wrong. It was 26 June and it was decided to do an exploratory operation. Mother gave consent to be kept on life support for 48 hours. While waiting to go into surgery she "communicated" with my sister and me all sorts of valuable information and we laughed a lot both with her and at her frustrations. She was on oxygen, without her glasses or hearing aid and with a nurse who had a limited command of English. Despite this, mother would not be beaten! She had always loved crosswords and our last few hours with her involved a lot of cryptic messages which my sister and I solved. Her last message stumped us both, but I think she would probably be rather pleased about that!

The surgery found nothing but the consultant felt that a further operation might just save her. Her kidneys and bowel were now failing. So we consented to another operation, and another 48 hours on life support, after which the life support machine was turned off and she died very peacefully.

In a strange way I was relieved and pleased. My mother had always feared growing old. Her father had gone blind; her mother had developed senile dementia and her brother had suffered from cancer – she was terrified of losing her independence and she didn't. Less than two weeks before she died, she was still working in the charity shop, mowing her lawns, doing her ironing and enjoying a gin and tonic and she was 79!

By early morning on 2 July, my euphoria about her death and the stress of her illness had taken its toll of me and I rang Dr Cembala who came out to see me. I knew I was in danger of another manic episode, as the treatment he had been giving me seemed to be having little effect. He and I had a rather bizarre interlude during which I thought I had agreed to be hospitalised, but he clearly thought I was no longer capable of giving rational consent and he had no choice but to have me sectioned. Clearly this is part of his job which he dreads…but so it was and the cavalry arrived once again: police, a social worker, another doctor and an ambulance. Just when I wanted to be allowed to grieve with what was left of my family, I was locked up in a mental health unit in a ward overlooking the room in which my mother had died. Sometimes life's a bitch!

As usual I was angry with the system and when I pointed out the irony of my situation, I was moved to a male ward! Have you ever tried to rest in a psychiatric unit in an un-lockable room surrounded by mentally ill males? I did, and I swear it is not possible even with sleeping tablets!

I was exhausted physically, emotionally and spiritually. At one point I collapsed and was physically sick on the carpet: one of the nurses accused me of making a mess and told me I would have to clear it up! This was compassion in England in 2004. Sometimes life beggars belief. I was, and am, lost for words.
I endured two weeks of hell but I did "respond to the medication" and was discharged on July 13. My mother's funeral was on July 14 and, although I hate speaking in public, I read one her favourite poems. Just as well I like a challenge!

I knew then that both my parents would have been very proud of me. My father was very fond of saying "Nil carborundum illegitimi" (which he always translated as "Don't let the b*******s grind you down"). Without a doubt, surviving that episode was the greatest achievement I have made since giving birth and, as I have said, six months later I pulled off another Christmas Tree Festival.

As we left church when it was all over, I swear I could hear a chuckle in the breeze and a distant voice muttering "You see, you don't know what you can do 'til you try!"…

15. Loving, hating and lashing out

When I was about 10, my maternal grandmother began suffering from senile dementia. She lived very close to us and my mother visited her twice a day most days. One of the things I remember most clearly about her mental deterioration was how she could become really vicious to my mother. There were times when she would come round to our house, in a confused state, in the middle of the night, expecting her dinner, and my mother would try and take her home to bed but she would become quite aggressive and often only my father could placate her and persuade her to go home with him. This was totally out of character as she and my mother had always been very close.

Now, unlike my grandmother, I grew up as a fiery red-head and spent many years learning to control my temper, so I cannot pretend that I am a stranger to lashing out orally but it is certainly not something I have made a habit of during my adult years.

I had known my future husband as a friend, for almost a year before we even went out together as a couple, and I remember being amazed at how quiet and placid he was. He once told me that he was quite shy and when he was with me he had no need to speak because I talked so much. (Some things don't change!)

However, since the onset of my illness, when I get really angry I go quiet. I will often burst into tears too, but my frustration and anger does eventually boil over and, of course, it is those closest to me, and those I love most, who bear the brunt of my tongue. My fuse is shorter and I am less tolerant of silly things which really don't matter.

As I have said before, I am extremely lucky to have survived the last 16 years, especially with my marriage intact, and that is in no small part due to the fact that I married this extremely placid, calm and emotionally stable man, who believes that marriage is "for better, for worse, for richer, for poorer, in sickness and in health". He is by no means perfect, but his attitude to me and my illness would take some beating!

On our 15th wedding anniversary he bought me a crystal 'book' called "Always" which came with a card that read: "When I said I do, I meant I do. I meant I will, I meant I always will" which sums up his philosophy of marriage. Despite his quietness he has a wonderful sense of humour which often allows him to defuse my anger.

When I am ill, and lashing out at him, he blames the illness, not me. For some reason every time I have been sectioned I have blamed him for having me locked up. Even after my mother died, when I rang my GP myself, I blamed him for me ending up in hospital with nothing but what I was standing up in! On that occasion, I was sectioned 19 years to the day since we got engaged and it certainly wasn't the way I would have chosen for us to spend the day.

In the past, when I have been sectioned, I have given him my wedding and engagement rings back and I have told staff that I don't wish to see him — I have punished him over and over again – and yet on a day-today basis he is the best, most stabilising influence in my life and we almost never argue! Obviously I find it hard to accept that I lash out at him in this way but it seems to be beyond my control. I have wondered whether it is because we are forced to be apart, at a time that I feel I really need his help and support that I do it. I can't blame the entire cavalry which arrives to section me as they disappear into thin air but he is always there to pick up the pieces and coax me back to normality.

My GP is much the same, I would love to blame him for having me sectioned, but once I am locked up he disappears until I am discharged. When I have questioned him about it, he too says "it's in the past, let bygones, be bygones" and he usually finds a way to make me laugh and move on. The bottom line is I hate the illness and what it does to me, but as he says "it is an illness, if it were diabetes, you would hate that too" and I know he is right.

In the longer term, I take comfort from the way my grandmother used to behave towards the daughter she loved dearly, and from the fact that many people suffering from mental illnesses also "turn against" those closest to them and those who care for them the most.

Just as I try not to dwell too much on the effect of my illness on my life, rather get on with living it, so my husband and I rarely look back at the worst times, we try and live in the present.

On a practical note, I have now made a list of items I would like brought to me if I am sectioned again and given it to my sister, my closest friend, and told my daughters where they can find a copy. By doing this, I hope that I will not be able to level "being locked up with nothing but what I am standing up in" at him again.

Footnote: *If you, or someone close to you, is suffering from manic depression, it might be worth trying to find ways to make the worst parts easier when they are in a calm and rational frame of mind.*
My worst case scenario is that my husband will die suddenly and I will be sectioned. I have also made a Power of Attorney so that someone else could deal with my affairs if necessary. For a long time I have "put off" facing my worst fears and discussing them with my family but now that I have, I feel better about it.

16. Picking up the pieces and facing the future – learning to ignore labels – working for Rethink

If you had asked me three years ago about my worst fears, one of them would have been losing my mother and having to sell the house which had been my home since I was three months old. I was very close to my mother, we were very similar in looks and temperament and coincidentally her birthday was the day after mine! (For many years, as a child, I was puzzled as to how I could have been born the day before her, I didn't realise then that there was about 30 years between us, but then maths never was my strong point!)

However awful the death of my mother was, and the hospital stay which followed, it was not as bad as I feared. I came out of the mental health unit totally focussed on her funeral the next day and that gave me a purpose. I was also almost half way through my university course and through planning the Christmas Tree Festival, so I had plenty to focus on. Because my mother had been so supportive both of my studying and the festival, I knew I must complete both. In September my sister and I cleared out our family home and put it on the market and on September 29 I sent off my final assignment. From then on I tackled the festival with gusto.

In saying this, I missed my mother greatly and still do. She was a tremendous support to me. She would arrive and do the ironing, gardening or cleaning, anything to make me take a break, but she was also an excellent role model. I look back to when my father died and she was so ill, and I wonder how she coped. At the time she said: "Life must go on. I must pick up the pieces and face the future" and so she did. As I have said she made herself busier than ever – if she had time on her hands, you would find her sewing a tapestry or battling with a jigsaw puzzle – her secret, she told me, was never to let herself wallow in self-pity.

I decided that the best tribute I could pay to her was to try and do the same.

It has not always been easy, I know she didn't ever profess it was easy, but I have tried to pick up the pieces and face the future without too much self-pity.

I was thrilled to get a Distinction in my studying but deeply saddened that my mother couldn't be with me when I received my certificate. (She hated hats, but she had been joking with me while she was ill, that I must finish the course so that she could treat herself to a hat for the presentation ceremony!) I tried to persuade my tutor to post the certificate to me, but she was reluctant and, in the end, I went to the University of Wales at Lampeter for two days with my husband (who bought a new suit!).

The Vice Chancellor presenting me with my Certificate in Interpersonal Skills for Volunteers at the University of Wales, Lampeter. Photograph courtesy of Matthew Scott.

My mother was fond of saying "as one door closes, so another opens" and in my case the "hat door" closed, but another opened as a result of my trip to Lampeter. We had a formal dinner on the first evening and I was seated next to the keynote speaker for presentation day - a lady called Jean Thompson who founded the Expert Patients Programme in this country. Now I had no idea who she was, or what the EPP was about, but suffice it to say EPP is for people with long-term health conditions and so I was very interested. The programme aims to help them learn new ways to manage their conditions. I have now been on the course, which consists of one half day over six weeks, and I have also been on a three day residential course and qualified as a volunteer tutor!

Almost certainly as a result of my studying at Lampeter, I got a paid job, with the charity Rethink, one day a week, working at a drop-in centre for people with severe mental illness. This was a real challenge for me but I thoroughly enjoyed it.

I introduced silk painting, which was very popular and successful, and I met some of the most interesting people I have ever been privileged to know. Each one of them has a far more interesting story to tell than mine, and I was greatly inspired by their courage in the face of day-to-day challenges. Just walking down the street some of them would be intimidated because they stood out from the crowd. Going on buses was out of the question during school runs because the kids would call them names…I could go on…but still they came to the centre where they were treated with dignity and kindness. Part of my job was to cook for the members on a rota basis – to be honest I found this far more stressful than befriending them!

Unfortunately, six months to the day that I started, there was an aggressive incident, triggered by a member of the public with a deep dislike of the drop-in centre, which undermined my confidence to such an extent that I left. I felt very guilty about leaving all the lovely but vulnerable people I had met, but I knew I must look after myself first.

The job had been a real eye-opener. I had never taken much notice of labels before, but through working with so many people whose diagnoses were so different, but whose symptoms were often very similar, it confirmed to me that what mattered was not the diagnosis but the person. Although I am not writing this as a direct result of my work there, it enabled me to look at my own illness in a much wider context. Without a doubt, had I not experienced mental illness myself I could not have done the job and if I had not met so many very special people my life would be much poorer.

17. Keep fit, keep taking the tablets and hope for the best

Before I went on the Expert Patients Programme I had bought myself an exercise machine. It is nothing elaborate, but it folds away neatly and allows me to get regular exercise without leaving the house! I had given up swimming and going to the gym because there were too many excuses I could make not to go, but I can find far fewer excuses to not spend half an hour exercising at home! It is basically a walking machine which causes minimal impact to my back.

I find that exercise is very good for me, especially in the morning and, although I can't pretend I enjoy it, by listening to music **(not** Michael Ball) I find it is quite relaxing. I really feel more energised and positive about the day so I have taken to getting out of bed, putting on a track suit or shorts and a T-shirt and doing half an hour on my machine before I shower and dress, and so far I have kept it up two or three times a week, most weeks, for six months. One of the problems with the Lithium Carbonate is that I have put on weight. I now weigh the same as I did when I was carrying the twins, 17 years ago, but I have lost half a stone in the last six months so the exercise regime is making me feel better in more ways than one!

Interestingly one of the modules on the EPP course looks at how exercise can help in the management of long-term health conditions, another looks at diet and I have been trying to take my diet in hand too.

I know that when I am depressed I eat for comfort; when I am manic I eat because I feel I need all the energy I can get; and otherwise I eat when I am bored or just because I like food! So I am trying to be much stricter about what, and when, I eat because I do realise it is important.

I have mentioned that I keep taking the tablets and I do, but I have tried to change my attitude to them. I used to regard them with disdain, almost as if they were poison. I think, because I took almost no medication before the onset of my illness, the concept of medication was fairly alien to me and I felt I should not need it, so I resented it and its side effects. Now I try and look on it as a valuable tool to help keep me well. I have a very pro-active approach to my illness now. I make sure I never run out of my medication and I keep a diary and make a note of my ups and downs and when my next check-up or next blood test is due and I remind my GP. It may sound silly, but it all makes me feel more in control of my illness.

Since the onset of my illness I have been hoping for the best and trying not to think about the worst, but now I am actively trying to be more positive in my outlook. I realised, while I was doing the EPP course, just how negative I had become. Each week on the programme we were encourage to make an "Action Plan", which was something we really wanted to achieve, and I set myself a target of thinking positively for just 15 minutes a day. I was surprised at how hard I found it but I did it and I have been working on positive thinking ever since. Over the years I have regularly felt defeated by very small things and I have felt unable to commit myself to anything because the illness had undermined my confidence to such an extent. The EPP course really helped to boost my confidence and my self-esteem and, one of my tutors, Julie Dennison, inspired me to write this book. She lives with epilepsy that is not controlled fully by drugs and she has written a book about living with her condition, so when I told her I was writing a book she was very encouraging, supportive and helpful.

At the end of the course we were encouraged to make a longer term goal and mine was to overcome my fear of flying. Since then I have planned a family holiday in Tuscany, which is now less than two weeks away. My daughters will finish their GCSE's next week and I wanted us all to have a really good break. This will be the first time I have flown any distance since they were born and, despite all my positive thinking, it is still quite daunting. I know that being sectioned has made me really claustrophobic and it is not taking off and landing I fear, it is feeling trapped in an aeroplane above the clouds. I know I will do it but I will be very glad when it is behind me! Perhaps, if I write anything else it should be called "Tuscany and beyond!"

As I found the Expert Patients Programme so valuable, I thought I would include a few basic details about it:
It is a national initiative developed in America and founded in this country in 2002 to help people living with long term health conditions maintain their health and improve their quality of life through lay-led self-

management courses. The courses are available **FREE** to anyone with a long-term health condition. Feed-back so far suggests:

- Participants have greater confidence in dealing with their illness
- Experience less pain and fatigue, depression and anxiety
- Persevere with exercise and relaxation techniques
- Make fewer visits to the GP
- Visit A & E departments less often
- Enjoy better communication with health professionals

Courses are run at local venues all over the country. For more information contact:
www.expertpatients.nhs.uk if you are not on the internet, ask your GP, local hospital or library if they can find details for you.

18. A blessing in disguise – compassionate teenagers!

Elsewhere in the book I have paid tribute to my husband and the way he has dealt with my illness but in this last chapter I would like pay tribute to my daughters. As the problems all started with their birth, it feels right to come full circle and end by talking about them.

As I have said, they were probably the single most important factor in my fighting to stay alive and, through all my mental torment, they have been a very positive reason to keep going.

When they were quite little and I was having a bad day they would say "mummy want chocolate?" as they grew older they would say "Mum needs a cup of tea (and/or) an emergency Mars bar!" Now they tend to offer to give me a manicure or to blow-dry my hair although they do ask if I need retail therapy too! Just before Christmas 2005 life was very stressful and they were "winding me up" and to quote them "I went off on one!" and had a lie down with Michael Ball. When I surfaced there was a note of apology and two mini Mars bars from a box of Celebrations sitting by the bed.

We have always been honest with them about my illness and we have never pretended that one day everything would be lovely again. That said, neither have we painted the future as very black. We have tried to explain that I suffer from a difficult and complicated illness but with their help we will cope and so we have.

They have learned to cope throughout all the ups and downs and they have developed their own mechanisms for dealing with me. Generally we have a very close relationship, but when I nag one of them or get angry with one they tend to unite against me! I know this is not uncommon with any children and certainly not twins but there have been times when I have blamed my illness for this.

Over the years I have worried a great deal about the effect my illness would have on them and sometimes when they are really angry with one another or me, I fear they are emulating me on a bad day! I remember one health professional telling me when they were very young that they would learn my behaviour and develop both manic and depressive tendencies from me - that really thrilled me!

I have to say, partially because of this, I was dreading the teenage years but, although I would never pretend they have been easy, so far, we are not half as hysterical and dysfunctional as I feared we would be.

The girls are very protective of me. They are very well attuned to my needs and they still have a very close relationship with their father. What surprises me even more is how many other people comment on how kind and helpful they are and how unusual it is to find not one, but two, teenagers who are lovely! Usually I do query if they mean my two, but I think that because they have seen suffering at close hand, they instinctively care about the "underdog". They have brokered a number of peace deals in relationships at school and have become actively involved, through their school, in a community project involving drug addicts and alcoholics. Their attitude has been really interesting. Like me, they have been more concerned with the individuals than the problems they have. They accept that just as anyone can become mentally ill, so anyone can become a drug addict or an alcoholic. The staff member in charge said he could not speak too highly of their attitude!

Not surprisingly then, they are extremely patient and loving towards their grandmother who is now 91 and suffering from senile dementia. They have friends with special needs and they automatically make allowances for their problems. One elderly lady summed them up by saying they were very compassionate, and that seems to me to be a very positive spin-off from my illness, which has to have been a blessing in disguise!

Having said all that, they are by no means perfect, but I love them dearly, and if they leave home in two years it will be very quiet without them and I shall have to make sure I don't become "a sad old woman" and make sure I "get a life or whatever!"

My daughters in 2007.

Some practical help for Depression

Whether or not you are on medication, it might be worth trying the following:

Breathing exercises
As you breathe in, and as you hold the breath, visualise that all this new, fresh, air is giving you new and positive energy. As you breathe out, slowly force out as many dark, sad and depressing thoughts as you can to make room in your body for the new ones.
Do this as often as you can. There is no life without breath and when you are depressed breathing often becomes shallow and laboured. If you feel like sighing in despair or frustration, think, as you do it, that all that negativity is leaving you and making room for your life to become more positive.

Did you know that when you cry tears are healing?
You don't always need "a shoulder to cry on". Crying alone can be helpful. Accepting and releasing the emotion is a way of managing your distress.
Letting tears flow washes out pain and, when you cry, your body releases tension and toxins and this helps to rebalance your emotions.
When you cry, try not to cry for too long as this may well make you look and feel awful. (I know I always end up with a blotchy red face and nose and a splitting headache!) Afterwards try washing your face in cold water, to reduce the redness, and then (if you are female) put on some make-up so you can face the world from behind a mask then go outside and speak to someone. (Even if you only comment on the weather, it will help you move on.)
This often works for me. I hope it works for you.

Postscript

Many years ago, long before my illness began, I remember reading that an opal is only made of sand and silica and it is nothing until it is broken and the light gets in and lets it emit the most beautiful rays. I have an opal in my engagement ring and I often wonder if, as humans, when we have been broken by mental illness, especially manic depression, we get a more beautiful perspective on life....

You can order further copies of:

"Double trouble...living with manic depression"
- a personal story and a practical guide
in 4 ways:
1. Online from: www.livingwithmanicdepression.com
2. From Rethink by tel: 0845 456 0455 or visit
   www.mentalhealthshop.org
3. By post from: Fourems Publications
   Business and Technology Centre
   Bessemer Drive
   Stevenage
   Herts SG1 2DX
4. By tel. from Books@Hoddesdon: 01992 442290

Please send me _____ copies of
"Double Trouble...living with manic depression"
(ISBN 978-0-9529765-6-1)

I enclose a UK bank cheque or postal order, payable to
Fourems Publications for £_____ £8.50 a copy (inc.
£1.00 p &p and a 50p donation to Rethink and MIND)
(PLEASE PRINT)

NAME: ....

ADDRESS: ....

....

....

POSTCODE: ....

This form may be photocopied. Please allow 28 days for
delivery. Do NOT send cash. Offer subject to availability.
We do not share or sell our customer's details.